C000229459

Gift of the C

ex libris

Candlestick Press

Published by:

Candlestick Press,
Diversity House, 72 Nottingham Road, Arnold, Nottingham UK NG5 6LF
www.candlestickpress.co.uk

Design and typesetting by Diversity Creative Marketing Solutions Ltd.,
www.diversity.agency

Printed by Ratcliff & Roper Print Group, Nottinghamshire, UK

Text by Eunice 'Pixie' Day

Illustrations, including cover © Kathy Morgan, 2017
www.kathymorganart.co.uk

Candlestick Press monogram © Barbara Shaw, 2008

Donation to Buttercups Goat Sanctuary www.buttercups.org.uk

ISBN 978 1 907598 56 2

Acknowledgements:

Candlestick Press wishes to thank Cheryl Astle, Cassie Astle and family
for their help and kind permission in publishing this story. Special thanks
are also due to Christine Ball and Goats-UK online forum members for
their support.

The text and poems in this pamphlet are reprinted from the following
books, all by permission of the publishers listed unless stated otherwise.
Every effort has been made to trace the copyright holders; however, the
editor and publisher apologise if any material has been included without
permission or without the appropriate acknowledgement, and would be
glad to be told of anyone who has not been consulted. Thanks are due to
all the copyright holders cited below for their kind permission:

This story was originally published in the *US Dairy Goat Journal*
(www.countrysidenetwork.com) (n.d.); later reprinted in the UK in the
British Goat Journal, January 2013, Vol. 106, pp.24-5, as 'The Gift of 'The
Old One''. Used with kind permission of the Estate of Eunice 'Pixie' Day
and Goats-UK online forum.

RS Thomas, *Collected Poems* (Orion, 2000), by permission of The Orion
Publishing Group.

James Stephens, *Reincarnations* (Literary Licensing, LLC, 2014) by
permission of The Society of Authors as the Literary Representatives of
the Estate of James Stephens.

Where poets are no longer living, their dates are given.

In memory of
Ch Sleigh Bell Farm Silver Sleet,
the original 'Old One'

The Coolin

Come with me, under my coat,
And we will drink our fill
Of the milk of the white goat,
Or wine if it be thy will;
And we will talk until
Talk is a trouble, too,
Out on the side of the hill,
And nothing is left to do,
But an eye to look into an eye
And a hand in a hand to slip,
And a sigh to answer a sigh,
And a lip to find out a lip:
What if the night be black
And the air on the mountain chill,
Where the goat lies down in her track
And all but the fern is still!
Stay with me under my coat,
And we will drink our fill
Of the milk of the white goat
Out on the side of the hill.

James Stephens (1880 – 1950)

Gift of the Old One

The young couple had made their usual hurried,
pre-Christmas visit to the little farm where dwelt their
elderly parents with their small herd
of goats. The farm had been named
Lone Pine Farm because of the
huge pine which topped the hill
behind the farm, and through
the years had become a
talisman to the old man and
his wife, and a landmark
in the countryside.

The old folks no longer
showed their goats, for
the years had taken their
toll, but they sold a little milk, and a few kids each year,
and the goats were their reason for joy in the morning and
contentment at day's end.

Crossly, as they prepared to leave, the young couple
confronted the old folks. "Why do you not at least dispose
of the 'Old One'? She is no longer of use to you. It's been
years since you've had either kids or milk from her. You
should cut corners and save where you can. Why do you
keep her anyway?"

The old man looked down as his worn boot scuffed at the barn floor and his arm stole defensively about the Old One's neck as he drew her to him and rubbed her gently behind the ears. He replied softly, "We keep her because of love. Only because of love."

Baffled and irritated, the young folks wished the old man and his wife a Merry Christmas and headed back toward the city as darkness stole through the valley.

So it was, that because of the leave-taking, no one noticed the insulation smouldering on the frayed wires in the old barn. None saw the first spark fall. None but the Old One.

In a matter of minutes, the whole barn was ablaze and the hungry flames were licking at the loft full of hay. With a cry of horror and despair, the old man shouted to his wife to call for help as he raced to the barn to save their beloved goats. But the flames were roaring now, and the blazing heat drove him back. He sank sobbing to the ground, helpless before the fire's fury.

By the time the fire department arrived, only smoking, glowing ruins were left, and the old man and his wife. They thanked those who had come to their aid, and the old man turned to his wife, resting her white head upon his shoulders as he clumsily dried her tears with a frayed red bandana.

Brokenly he whispered, "We have lost much, but God has spared our home on this eve of Christmas. Let us, therefore, climb the hill to the old pine where we have sought comfort in times of despair. We will look down upon our home and give thanks to God that it has been spared."

And so, he took her by the hand and helped her up the snowy hill as he brushed aside his own tears with the back of his hand. As they stepped over the little knoll at the crest of the hill, they looked up and gasped in amazement at the incredible beauty before them. Seemingly, every glorious, brilliant star in the heavens was caught up in the glittering, snow-frosted branches of their beloved pine, and it was aglow with heavenly candles. And poised on its topmost bough, a crystal crescent moon glistened like spun glass. Never had a mere mortal created a Christmas tree such as this. Suddenly, the old man gave a cry of wonder and incredible joy as he pulled his wife forward. There, beneath the tree, was their Christmas gift.

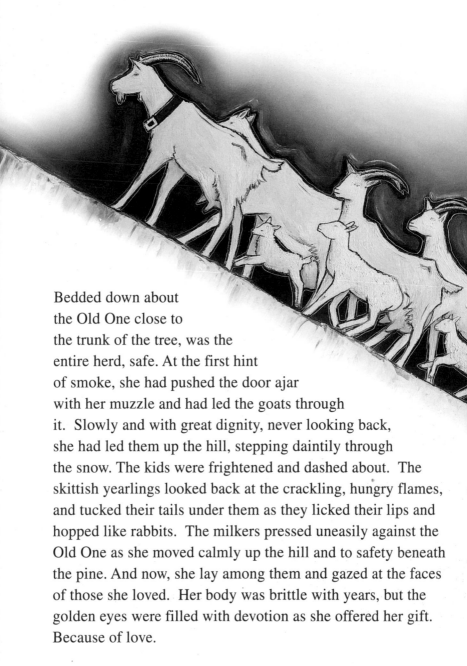

Bedded down about
the Old One close to
the trunk of the tree, was the
entire herd, safe. At the first hint
of smoke, she had pushed the door ajar
with her muzzle and had led the goats through
it. Slowly and with great dignity, never looking back,
she had led them up the hill, stepping daintily through
the snow. The kids were frightened and dashed about. The
skittish yearlings looked back at the crackling, hungry flames,
and tucked their tails under them as they licked their lips and
hopped like rabbits. The milkers pressed uneasily against the
Old One as she moved calmly up the hill and to safety beneath
the pine. And now, she lay among them and gazed at the faces
of those she loved. Her body was brittle with years, but the
golden eyes were filled with devotion as she offered her gift.
Because of love.

Only because of love.

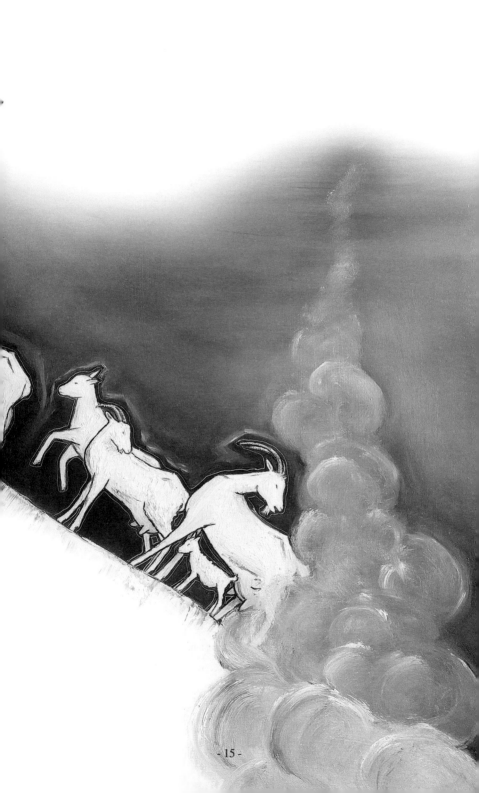

Gift

Some ask the world
    and are diminished
in the receiving
    of it. You gave me

only this small pool
    that the more I drink
from, the more overflows
    me with sourceless light.

RS Thomas (1913 – 2000)